From Grandmother With Love

FROM GRANDMOTHER WITH LOVE

A LIFE RECALLED FOR MY GRANDCHILD

WRITTEN BY JANE PETTIGREW
ILLUSTRATED BY MARY WOODIN

LITTLE, BROWN AND COMPANY
Boston · Toronto · London

First published in Great Britain in 1992 by
Little, Brown and Company (UK) Limited
Brigade House, 8 Parsons Green, London SW6 4TN.

Designed by Lisa Tai

ISBN 0-316-88888-5

A CIP catalogue record for this book is available
from the British Library

10 9 8 7 6 5 4 3 2 1

Typeset by Central Southern Typesetters, Eastbourne
Colour separation by Fotographics, Hong Kong
Printed and bound in Belgium by Brepols, Turnhout

$\mathscr{W}$ith love from _____

$\mathscr{T}$o _____

$\mathscr{D}$ate _____

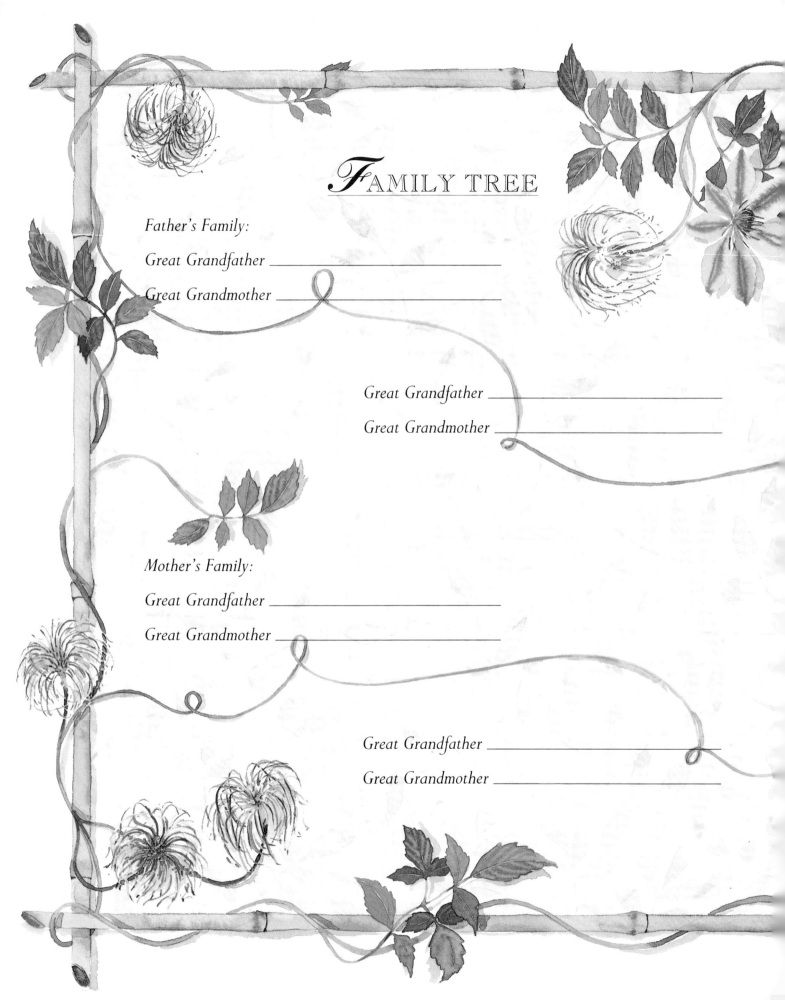

FAMILY TREE

Father's Family:

Great Grandfather _____

Great Grandmother _____

Great Grandfather _____

Great Grandmother _____

Mother's Family:

Great Grandfather _____

Great Grandmother _____

Great Grandfather _____

Great Grandmother _____

Grandfather _____

Grandmother _____

Father _____

Grandchild _____

Mother _____

Grandfather _____

Grandmother _____

$\mathcal{M}$Y GRANDPARENTS

My mother's family

My grandfather's name _____

My grandmother's name _____

They were married _____

_____

They lived in _____

_____

My grandfather's job _____

_____

My father's family

My grandfather's name _____

My grandmother's name _____

They were married _____

_____

They lived in _____

_____

My grandfather's job _____

_____

$\mathcal{M}$Y PARENTS

My father's name _____

Date of birth _____

Place of birth _____

My mother's name _____

Date of birth _____

Place of birth _____

How they met _____

_____

_____

They were married

Date _____

Place _____

After they married, they lived _____

_____

_____

Their jobs _____

_____

_____

*photograph of
your grandmother
as a young girl*

$\mathcal{I}$ WAS BORN

I was born:

Date _____

Place _____

I weighed _____

My parents named me _____

_____

My parents told me later that _____

_____

_____

_____

_____

My brothers and sisters _____

_____

_____

_____

_____

_____

$\mathcal{M}$Y EARLY CHILDHOOD

When I was a little girl:

My family lived _____

My favourite toys were _____

_____

_____

My favourite stories were _____

_____

I liked playing _____

_____

_____

I started school when I was _____

My childhood quirks _____

_____

_____

Things I remember about my parents _____

_____

_____

_____

$\mathscr{M}$Y SCHOOLDAYS

My first school was ————————————————————

My school uniform was ————————————————

My best lesson was ——————————————————

My favourite teachers were ————————————————

————————————————————————————

My best friends were ————————————————————

————————————————————————————

At playtime we ——————————————————————

————————————————————————————

Things I remember about my first school ————————————

————————————————————————————

————————————————————————————

————————————————————————————

————————————————————————————

————————————————————————————

————————————————————————————

————————————————————————————

My secondary school was _____

The uniform was _____

_____

My favourite subjects were _____

_____

My favourite teachers were _____

_____

Teachers could punish us by _____

_____

Prizes were awarded for _____

_____

At lunchtime I _____

_____

Sports I played at school _____

_____

Clubs I belonged to _____

_____

Special positions I held _____

_____

_____

$\mathcal{M}$Y TEENAGE YEARS

When I was a teenager my family lived _____

_____

My ambitions _____

_____

_____

In my spare time I _____

_____

_____

At weekends I _____

_____

_____

My best friends were _____

_____

I liked to spend money on _____

_____

_____

My money came from _____

_____

The fashion rage was _____

_____

_____

_____

What I remember about boyfriends _____

_____

_____

_____

_____

Things that used to make me happy _____

_____

_____

_____

Things that used to upset me _____

_____

_____

When I left school I _____

_____

_____

_____

THINGS I LIKED BEST

My favourite:

Record _____

Singer _____

Actor _____

Actress _____

Play or film _____

Radio or television programme _____

_____

Book _____

Sport _____

Activity _____

Food _____

Drink _____

Season _____

Colour _____

Holiday _____

Fashion _____

Flower _____

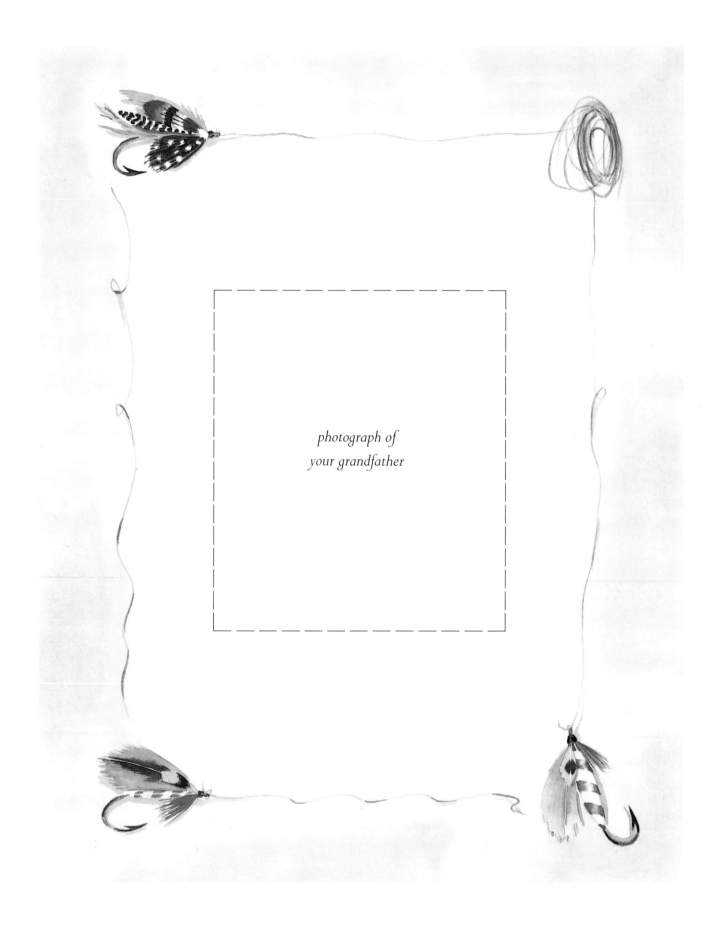

*photograph of
your grandfather*

YOUR GRANDFATHER'S YOUTH

Grandfather was born:

Date _____

Place _____

His full name _____

His family lived _____

_____

His parents' jobs _____

_____

_____

He went to school _____

_____

_____

His hobbies were _____

_____

_____

His ambitions were _____

_____

_____

WHEN I MET YOUR GRANDFATHER

Grandfather and I met _____

_____

_____

My age _____

His age _____

Our first date was _____

_____

_____

I liked him because _____

_____

He said he liked me because _____

_____

We liked to go _____

_____

_____

We decided to get married _____

_____

_____

*photograph of
our wedding*

OUR WEDDING

Your grandfather and I were married:

Date _____

Place _____

He wore _____

_____

His best man was _____

I wore _____

_____

My flowers were _____

_____

My bridesmaids/pages were _____

_____

_____

They wore _____

_____

I was given away by _____

photograph of reception
or honeymoon

Our wedding reception was held at _____

_____

Number of guests _____

Our favourite wedding present was _____

_____

_____

The things I remember most clearly about the day _____

_____

_____

_____

_____

For our honeymoon we _____

_____

_____

_____

OUR FIRST YEARS TOGETHER

When we were first married, your grandfather and I lived in _____

_____

_____

We lived there for _____

Things I liked and disliked about our first home _____

_____

_____

_____

Your grandfather's job was _____

_____

I spent my time _____

_____

_____

In the evenings and at weekends we liked to _____

_____

_____

_____

_____

*photograph of your
parent as a baby*

𝒴OUR PARENT WAS BORN

Your parent was born:

Date _____

Place _____

Full name _____

Colour of hair at birth _____

Weight at birth _____

We thought our baby looked like _____

_____

Favourite toy _____

First word _____

Nickname _____

Childhood quirks _____

_____

_____

Brothers and sisters _____

_____

_____

_____

Your parent's childhood

Junior school ————————————————

Secondary school ————————————————

Best subject at school ————————————————

————————————————————————

Interests and hobbies ————————————————

————————————————————————

————————————————————————

Favourite activities ————————————————

————————————————————————

Ambitions ————————————————

————————————————————————

Favourite music ————————————————

————————————————————————

Favourite fashion ————————————————

————————————————————————

Favourite sport ————————————————

We were strict about ————————————————

————————————————————————

photograph of your parents' wedding

𝒴OUR PARENTS

Your mother and father met _____

_____

_____

_____

They were married

Date _____

Place _____

Time _____

The reception was held at _____

_____

_____

For their honeymoon they _____

_____

_____

What I remember best about the day _____

_____

_____

_____

photograph of
you as a baby

YOU WERE BORN

You were born:

Date _____

Time _____

Place _____

You weighed _____

When I heard the news I _____

_____

_____

I first saw you _____

_____

_____

_____

My first thoughts about you were _____

_____

_____

_____

_____

$\mathscr{Y}$OUR GRANDMOTHER TODAY

My interests and hobbies _____

_____

_____

_____

Things I like about life today _____

_____

_____

_____

Things I dislike about life today _____

_____

_____

_____

Things I regret _____

_____

_____

Things I still hope to do _____

_____

_____

THINGS I LIKE BEST TODAY

My favourite:

Music _____

Television programme _____

Radio programme _____

Actor _____

Actress _____

Entertainer _____

Film _____

Book _____

Food _____

Drink _____

Fashion _____

Colour _____

Holiday resort _____

Activity _____

Time of day _____

Season _____

Flower _____

photograph of
your grandfather

$\mathcal{A}$LL ABOUT YOUR GRANDFATHER

His job _____

_____

_____

His ambitions _____

_____

_____

His interests and hobbies _____

_____

His friends _____

_____

His likes and dislikes _____

_____

His favourite sport _____

_____

His favourite food and drink _____

_____

His favourite activity _____

_____

$\mathcal{T}$HEN AND NOW

How the world has changed since I was a girl:

Inventions _____

_____

_____

Discoveries _____

_____

_____

Attitudes to money _____

_____

Attitudes to women _____

_____

Attitudes to children _____

_____

Manners _____

_____

_____

Travel _____

_____

Entertainment _____

_____

_____

Shopping _____

_____

_____

Education _____

_____

_____

Housing _____

_____

_____

Holidays _____

_____

_____

Clothes and hair styles _____

_____

_____

Gadgets _____

_____

UNFORGETTABLE HOLIDAYS

FAMILY CELEBRATIONS

Festivity _____

Date _____

We celebrate this occasion by _____

_____

_____

The special foods we eat are _____

_____

_____

Festivity _____

Date _____

We celebrate this occasion by _____

_____

_____

The special foods we eat are _____

_____

_____

Festivity _____

Date _____

We celebrate this occasion by _____

_____

_____

_____

The special foods we eat are _____

_____

_____

Festivity _____

Date _____

We celebrate this occasion by _____

_____

_____

_____

The special foods we eat are _____

_____

_____

FAMILY RECIPES

FAMILY RECIPES

FAMILY ACCIDENTS AND AILMENTS

_____

_____

_____

_____

_____

_____

_____

_____

_____

_____

_____

_____

_____

_____

_____

_____

OUR RELATIVES

Name _____

Relationship _____

```
photograph
```

Name _____

Relationship _____

```
photograph
```

Name _____

Relationship _____

```
photograph
```

Name _____

Relationship _____

```
photograph
```

Name _____

Relationship _____

```
┌ ─ ─ ─ ─ ─ ─ ─ ─ ┐
│                 │
│                 │
│   photograph    │
│                 │
│                 │
└ ─ ─ ─ ─ ─ ─ ─ ─ ┘
```

Name _____

Relationship _____

```
┌ ─ ─ ─ ─ ─ ─ ─ ─ ┐
│                 │
│                 │
│   photograph    │
│                 │
│                 │
└ ─ ─ ─ ─ ─ ─ ─ ─ ┘
```

Name _____

Relationship _____

```
┌ ─ ─ ─ ─ ─ ─ ─ ─ ┐
│                 │
│                 │
│   photograph    │
│                 │
│                 │
└ ─ ─ ─ ─ ─ ─ ─ ─ ┘
```

Name _____

Relationship _____

```
┌ ─ ─ ─ ─ ─ ─ ─ ─ ┐
│                 │
│                 │
│   photograph    │
│                 │
│                 │
└ ─ ─ ─ ─ ─ ─ ─ ─ ┘
```

NOTES AND PHOTOGRAPHS

NOTES AND PHOTOGRAPHS

Notes and Photographs